Chal...
and
Relaxed Ravina

by HANSA PANKHANIA
Illustrations by Anne-Marie Sonneveld

GW00859378

Published by SOHUM PUBLICATIONS

Chakraji and Relaxed Ravina
by Hansa Pankhania
© Hansa Pankhania 2021

Illustrations and book design by Anne-Marie Sonneveld
www.ams-illustrations.com

ISBN 978-1-914201-02-8

The moral right to be identified as the author of this work has been
asserted by Hansa Pankhania in accordance with the Designs and Copyrights Act 1988.

All rights reserved. No part of this publication may be reproduced, stored in retrival
system, or transmitted, in any form or by any means without the prior written
permission of the publisher, nor be otherwise circulated in any form
of binding or cover than that in which it is published and without similar condition
being imposed on the subsequent purchaser.
A CIP catalogue record for this book is available at the British Library.

Ravina is in the school playground, sulking in a corner. She is upset because nobody will play with her.

The girl she thought was her friend does not want to be her friend anymore.

1

Ravina walks up to the trees on the edge of the playground. She lies down. She closes her eyes to shut out her troubles.

Suddenly,
a beautiful swan
appears
from behind her
and says,

"Ravina, I can see you are upset.
I'm here to help you."

3

"Come and sit on my back and I will take you
to a place where your upset will be gone, gone, gone."

4

Ravina slowly climbs
onto the swan's back.

5

They swim along a beautiful river
with crystal clear water.

The fields
on either side glow
with shades of green and gold.

Soon, they spot a bridge ahead
in beautiful rainbow colours.

As they get nearer,
Ravina can see someone dressed
in gold and white robes with long,
black, curly hair, sitting comfortably
at the top of the bridge.

8

They stop beside the lady. The swan tells Ravina, "This is Chakraji. She knows what is troubling you and will make your upset disappear."

Chakraji talks in a soft, kind voice.
"Ravina, first sit quietly and close your eyes."

"Now, let's start
by relaxing
your FACE."

"Then relax each part of your body very slowly."

"Relax your

NECK

SHOULDERS

CHEST

ARMS

FINGERS

TUMMY

BACK

LEGS

and lastly,
your FEET."

13

"Feel all your troubles seeping out of your toes into the water below and disappearing forever.

Let's do this one more time. You can repeat this until your upset is gone, gone, gone."

Ravina and Chakraji practise again.

Ravina slowly starts to feel relaxed
in her body and begins to smile. 15

"Ravina, you can pass on this magic to your friends and to anyone else who may need help."

The swan and Ravina say goodbye to Chakraji before beginning their return journey.

On their way back, the swan says to Ravina,
"Have faith in you. Do the relaxation that Chakraji
has taught you. If you want even more help, then keep saying
these magic words in your mind all day."

I WILL FIND NEW FRIENDS,
I AM LOVED,
I AM RELAXED

Ravina opens her eyes, and is
back in the corner
of the playground.
She stumbles
as she tries to get up. 19

A girl from her class sees her and says,
"Are you okay? Let me help you."

They smile at each other
as Ravina thanks her for her help.

Ravina is not worried now. She knows how to make her troubles disappear and how to pass on her magic. She whispers the swan's magic words to herself.

I WILL FIND NEW FRIENDS

I AM LOVED

I AM RELAXED

She sits quietly
and relaxes each part of
her body very slowly.

She does this again until all her upset is
GONE, GONE, GONE!

*I dedicate this book
to my future generations.*

My deep-felt gratitude
to my family and friends
for their love and encouragement.

The Chakraji series of children's books
was written during a writing retreat on a barge
with my colleagues from Solihull Writers Group.

Special thanks to Robert Ferguson,
Dawn Bolton, Isabelle Walker
and Jacqueline Horton for their support.

Note for Parents and Teachers

While reading with your children, practice the breathing and affirmations with them. This will be helpful in demonstrating the techniques. It may surprise you when you also feel calm and relaxed, as the techniques are equally helpful for adults. There is more to the pictures and words in this book hence you are encouraged to have conversations to help develop your child's interest and understanding.

These techniques are passed on in good faith. The author and the publisher are not liable for any contraindications. This book is not intended as a substitute for medical advice. If in any doubt, please consult your doctor before practicing the techniques.

This book is the second in the series of **Six Chakraji Books**, helping children to address stress by learning practical, natural coping techniques. The first book in this series is *Chakraji and Calm Callum*. The next in this series will be *Chakraji and Peaceful Peter*.

Chakraji and Relaxed Ravina

Children may not have the capability to articulate distress, hence it is important to find creative and natural ways of helping them express negative emotions and ways of overcoming these. By learning these skills at an early age, it may prevent the development of mental health issues in later life.

The Chakraji series of children's picture books uses imaginative storytelling, to help children articulate and manage stressful situations. This is done by introducing natural breathing and mindfulness-based practical techniques, that a child will find easy to use and benefit from.

The techniques are equally helpful for parents, who are encouraged to demonstrate while reading through the book and having conversations after reading.

The aim is that the child will learn to integrate this way of helping to alleviate stress, making this a spontaneous response to difficult situations. This series of Chakraji books introduces a range of different mindfulness-based breathing, relaxation and positive affirmation techniques, to enable children to build a repertoire of coping skills that can help manage stress throughout their life.

Chakraji and Relaxed Ravina
TESTIMONIALS

A brilliant, engaging short story, filled with superb, vibrant illustrations. Mindfulness is such an important life tool. Introducing this concept at a young age can not only foster a positive and healthier mindset for children but also for adults too. Chakraji and Relaxed Ravina elegantly captures the essence of mindfulness in a practical way which children can relate to.
Dr Seeta Raja - GP

Hansa Pankhania subtlety introduces the inevitable harsh realities of the real world to delicate minds of young children, at the same time as giving them simple yet powerful tools to handle these. Chakraji and Relaxed Ravina is a must-have for all children and their parents.
Neha Verma - a new mother.

I found myself feeling really emotional as I reached the end of the book. I am a retired engineer and do not normally feel this way with books! You have put some magic into the story, Hansa. So many adults and children can benefit from Chakraji and Relaxed Ravina. There is a real need for this book in school libraries across the country.
David Waite - Counsellor

The Chakraji stories are a brilliant resource for teaching children how to deal with their stress and anxiety, whether during a period of world crisis or just dealing with the ups and downs of daily life.
Josephine Lay - Poet and Author (MA in Writing for Young People)

I wish I had been taught these skills as a child, as I struggle with anxiety as an adult. I will ensure my children do these techniques. Hansa has a gift of passing on small nuggets of wisdom that can help children as well as adults.
El Wing

Chakraji and Relaxed Ravina is a wonderful children's book with a beautiful message. Chakraji helps Ravina to manage her challenging emotions and talk to herself in a positive way to overcome her friendship worries. This story is relatable for all children. This simple technique is suitable for all ages and is a wonderful life skill to be equipped with.
Debra Webster - Co-Founder of Emotions Toolkit and Ex- Primary School Teacher

This book is beautifully illustrated, and I think it will be a great tool to help children learn relaxation techniques.
Penny Hackney - Founder- Matthew Hackney Foundation

My daughter loves Chakraji. I also think she is beautiful, kind and helpful. We all need a friend like that in our lives!
B. Kaur - Parent

I read this story to my grandson. We had great fun with the relaxation practice. Aside from my grandson, I had the best night's sleep after doing the techniques with him!
John A - Grandfather

About the Author

HANSA PANKHANIA writes wellbeing books for adults and children. She also offers consultancy, training and coaching helping you to have a life full of happiness, enjoy perfect health and achieve your dream goals.
She has a burning passion to make a positive difference in people's lives and is compelled to write words which trigger seismic positive changes in your life.

The books and blogs Hansa writes guide you to integrate small and remarkably simple practices in your day that will nourish your body, mind, and soul, enabling peace with all aspects of your being.

For workshops and coaching, plus access to FREE resources on enjoying a stress-free and happy life, visit:

www.aumconsultancy.co.uk
or text **+44(0)7888747438**

Please share to support our campaign for better mental health for adults and children.

Lightning Source UK Ltd.
Milton Keynes UK
UKHW050839290421
382777UK00006B/53

9 781914 201028